Exploring Planets
NEPTUNE

Susan Ring

WEIGL PUBLISHERS INC.

Published by Weigl Publishers Inc.
350 5th Avenue, Suite 3304, PMB 6G
New York, NY USA 10118-0069
Web site: www.weigl.com
Copyright 2004 WEIGL PUBLISHERS INC.

Library of Congress Cataloging-in-Publication Data

Ring, Susan.
  Neptune / by Susan Ring.
      v. cm. -- (Exploring planets)
Includes index.
Contents: Introducing Neptune -- What's in a name? -- Neptune spotting
-- Early observations -- Neptune in the solar system -- Neptune and
Earth -- Missions to Neptune -- Neptune explorer: Urbain Leverrier --
Neptune explorer: Dr. Matthew Hill -- Neptune on the web -- Activity:
Neptune language arts -- What have you learned?
  ISBN 1-59036-102-4 (lib. bdg. : alk. paper) – ISBN 1-59036-229-2 (pbk.)
  1. Neptune (Planet)--Juvenile literature. [1. Neptune (Planet)] I.
Title. II. Series.
  QB691 .R56 2003
  523.48'1--dc21
                              2002014563

Printed in the United States of America
1 2 3 4 5 6 7 8 9 0 08 07 06 05 04

Photograph Credits
Every reasonable effort has been made to trace ownership and to obtain permission to reprint
copyright material. The publishers would be pleased to have any errors or omissions brought
to their attention so that they may be corrected in subsequent printings.

Cover: NASA (top); Digital Vision (bottom)

ArtToday.com, Inc.: page 21; **Virginia Boulay:** pages 8, 12; **CORBIS/MAGMA:** pages 17, 18 (Arthur
Thévenart); **Corel Corporation:** page 6; **Digital Vision:** pages 9, 14L, 14R, 22; **Hulton|Archive by
Getty Images:** pages 10, 11; **NASA:** pages 1, 4, 7, 19; **Visuals Unlimited:** page 13.

Project Coordinator Jennifer Nault **Design** Terry Paulhus **Substantive Editor** Frances Purslow
Copy Editor Janice Redlin **Layout** Bryan Pezzi **Photo Researcher** Tina Schwartzenberger

Contents

Introducing Neptune

Neptune is one of the coldest planets in our **solar system**. It is also one of the four gas giants. These are planets in our solar system that are formed mainly of gas. Long ago, people did not know that Neptune existed. The planet was discovered in 1846. Many of the other planets in our solar system had already been discovered. We are learning new things about Neptune every day.

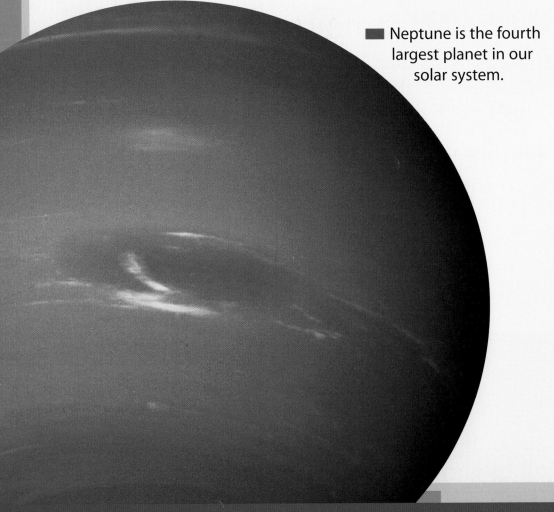

Neptune is the fourth largest planet in our solar system.

Neptune Facts

- Methane gas in Neptune's **atmosphere** makes the planet appear blue.

- Neptune has the strongest and fastest winds in our solar system. Winds reach speeds of 1,500 miles (2,414 kilometers) per hour.

- Each summer and winter on Neptune lasts 41 years.

- Neptune has rings made of dust.

- Neptune's rings were first spotted from Earth about 20 years ago.

- One of Neptune's moons, Triton, is bigger than the planet Pluto. Neptune's smallest moon, Naiad, is only 36 miles (58 km) wide.

- Neptune has its own heat source. It makes twice as much heat as it receives from the Sun.

Name That Planet

What does the name *Neptune* mean? In Roman **mythology**, Neptune is the god of the sea. In Greek mythology, Neptune is named Poseidon.

People believed that Neptune's quick temper was responsible for storms and earthquakes. Sailors often blamed him for causing storms at sea.

Neptune is usually shown holding a three-pointed tool called a trident. Fish and dolphins often surround him.

■ Neptune, god of the sea, is also known as the god of horses and horse racing.

Neptune Moons

Scientists have found eight moons around Neptune. The planet's largest moon is called Triton. Triton **orbits** Neptune in the opposite direction from the other moons. Triton is also the coldest place in our solar system. The temperature on Triton can fall to −391° Fahrenheit (−235° C).

■ British **astronomer** William Lassell first discovered Triton in 1846.

Neptune Spotting

Neptune is the eighth planet from the Sun, but sometimes it becomes the ninth. Although this switch in position seems unusual, there is a reason. Every 248 years, Pluto passes inside Neptune's orbit. When this occurs, Neptune becomes the farthest planet from the Sun. This switch last happened between 1979 and 1999.

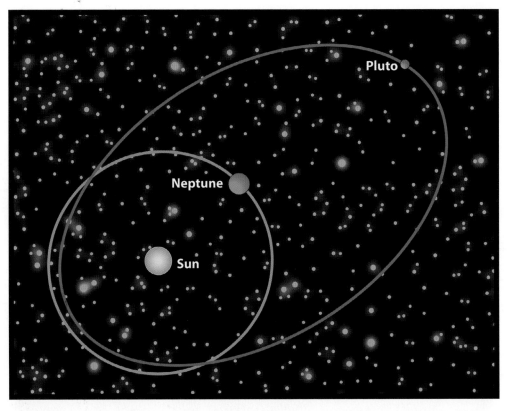

■ Neptune becomes the farthest planet from the Sun when its orbit crosses beyond Pluto's odd-shaped orbit.

See for Yourself

If you look up at the sky at night, you will not see
Neptune. The planet can only be seen with a telescope
or strong binoculars. Even then, Neptune appears very
small. If you know where to look, you can see the planet
shining like a bright, blue star. Ask science center staff
for the best times to view Neptune.

■ Neptune is always
found in the same
region of Earth's sky.

Early Observations

In 1613, an Italian astronomer saw Neptune through his telescope. That man, Galileo Galilei, thought he had seen a star. When he observed the object, clouds were covering his view of the sky. Galileo did not notice that the object changed position in the sky. He would have known it was a planet if he had seen it moving. Neptune was not discovered for more than 200 years after Galileo's sighting.

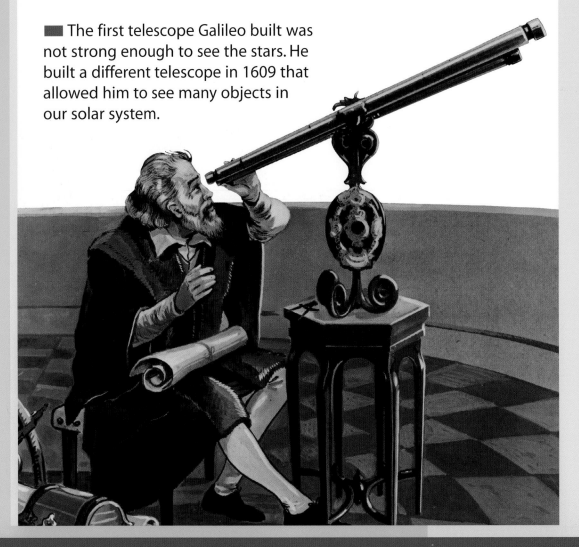

■ The first telescope Galileo built was not strong enough to see the stars. He built a different telescope in 1609 that allowed him to see many objects in our solar system.

John Couch Adams

John Couch Adams was born in England in 1819. He became a **mathematician** when he grew up. John became interested in an astronomical problem. He noticed that something kept pulling Uranus off its orbit. He thought that it must be the **gravity** of another planet. Using math, John **predicted** the location of this mysterious planet. Although nobody believed him at the time, John's prediction was correct. The mysterious planet was Neptune.

■ John Couch Adams's prediction was proved correct when Neptune was discovered in 1846.

Neptune in Our Solar System

Neptune is one of the nine planets in our solar system.
It is the eighth planet from the Sun.

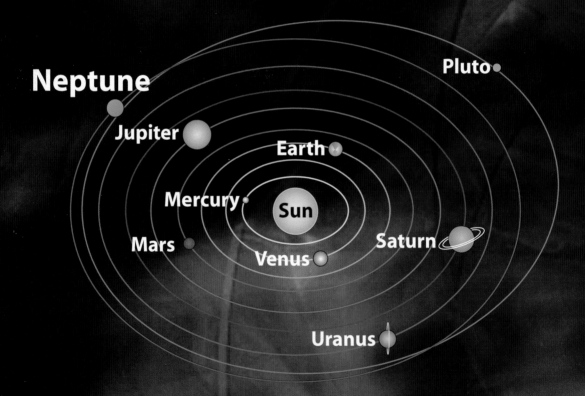

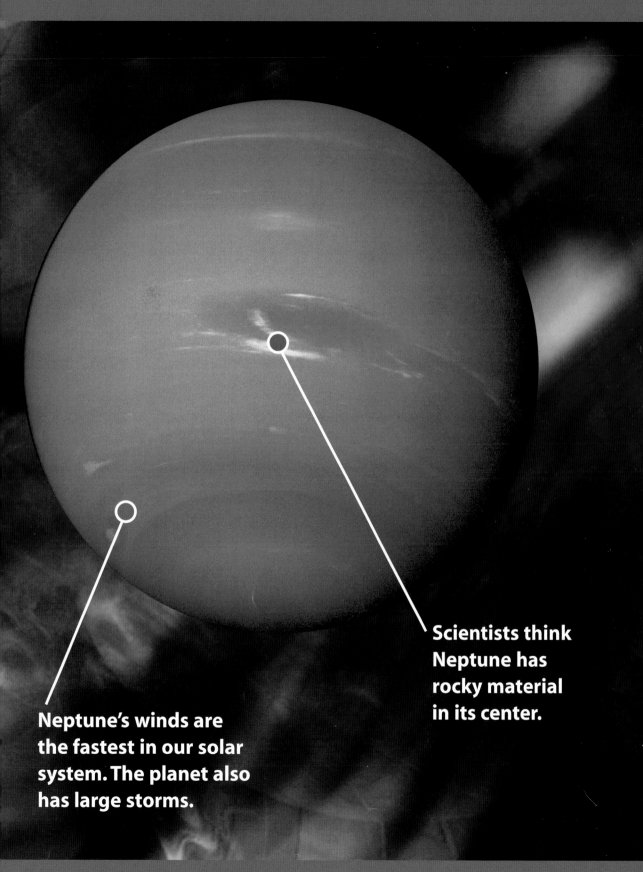

Scientists think Neptune has rocky material in its center.

Neptune's winds are the fastest in our solar system. The planet also has large storms.

Neptune and Earth

Neptune is much larger than Earth. Its **diameter** is about four times Earth's diameter. Neptune is also much colder than Earth. This is because Neptune is very far from the Sun. It is thirty times farther from the Sun than Earth.

Earth is known as a rocky planet because it is solid. Neptune is made up of gases, so it is not solid. There is no ground to stand on. Scientists believe that the gas planets developed differently than the rocky planets.

Neptune is seventy-two times the size of Earth. Even though it is much bigger in size, Neptune's **mass** is only seventeen times the mass of Earth.

Compare the Planets

PLANET FEATURES

PLANET	Distance from the Sun	Days to Orbit the Sun	Diameter	Length of Day	Average Temperature
Mercury	36 million miles (58 million km)	88	3,032 miles (4,880 km)	4,223 hours	333° Fahrenheit (167° C)
Venus	67 million miles (108 million km)	225	7,521 miles (12,104 km)	2,802 hours	867° Fahrenheit (464° C)
Earth	93 million miles (150 million km)	365	7,926 miles (12,756 km)	24 hours	59° Fahrenheit (15° C)
Mars	142 million miles (229 million km)	687	4,222 miles (6,795 km)	25 hours	−81° Fahrenheit (−63° C)
Jupiter	484 million miles (779 million km)	4,331	88,846 miles (142,984 km)	10 hours	−230° Fahrenheit (−146° C)
Saturn	891 million miles (1,434 million km)	10,747	74,897 miles (120,535 km)	11 hours	−285° Fahrenheit (−176° C)
Uranus	1,785 million miles (2,873 million km)	30,589	31,763 miles (51,118 km)	17 hours	−355° Fahrenheit (−215° C)
Neptune	2,793 million miles (4,495 million km)	59,800	30,775 miles (49,528 km)	16 hours	−355° Fahrenheit (−215° C)
Pluto	3,647 million miles (5,869 million km)	90,588	1,485 miles (2,390 km)	153 hours	−375° Fahrenheit (−226° C)

Missions to Neptune

So far, *Voyager 2* is the only **space probe** to study Neptune. Before *Voyager 2*, scientists thought Neptune only had two moons. Six more were discovered by the space probe.

In 1989, *Voyager 2* discovered a hole in Neptune's atmosphere. The hole was as large as Earth. Scientists named it the Great Dark Spot. Oddly, in 1994, the spot had disappeared. Later, another dark spot was found.

U.S. MISSION TO NEPTUNE			
Space Probe	**Launched**	**Purpose**	**Results**
Voyager 2	1977	flyby	Took 10,000 photographs; discovered moons and rings

Voyager 2 is still in space. It is speeding through our solar system at 36,000 miles (58,000 km) per hour. In 2002, the probe was farther away from Earth than the last planet in our solar system, Pluto.

Scooter Power

"Scooter" is the name scientists have given to a bright, wispy spot on Neptune. This spot was photographed by *Voyager 2*. In the photographs, Scooter was located below the Great Dark Spot. It changes shape and moves around the planet. Scientists do not know for certain what Scooter is.

■ Photographs taken by *Voyager 2* helped astronomers discover Neptune's four rings and six additional moons.

Planet People

Urbain Le Verrier

Name: Urbain Le Verrier
Neptune Accomplishments: Predicted that there was another planet beyond Uranus

In 1846, a French mathematician named Urbain Le Verrier was studying the sky. Like John Couch Adams, Urbain saw that something was affecting Uranus's orbit. Urbain predicted that another planet's gravity was responsible. Urbain told an astronomer his idea. Three months later, Le Verrier received a letter from the astronomer. The letter read, "The planet whose position you have pointed out actually exists." Today, both John Couch Adams and Urbain Le Verrier are given credit for Neptune's discovery.

■ A statue of Urbain Le Verrier stands outside the Paris Royal Observatory.

Heidi Hammel

Name: Heidi Hammel
Neptune Accomplishments:
Researches Neptune's storms

Heidi Hammel works with other astronomers to find out why Neptune has such fierce storms. When Heidi was a child, she enjoyed learning about space objects.

Heidi is an astronomer and a professor at the Massachusetts Institute of Technology. She researches Neptune's storms. Photographs taken by *Voyager 2* show that Neptune has a stormy **climate**. Neptune's storms are much stronger than scientists had thought. They assumed that Neptune's climate would be calm because it is so far from the Sun.

Voyager 2 was launched from the NASA Kennedy Space Center in Florida on August 20, 1977.

Neptune on the Internet

To learn more about Neptune, look for books at your school library. The Internet is also an excellent place to learn about Neptune. There are many great Web sites with information. Just type the words *Neptune* and *planet* into a search engine. Google and Yahoo are useful search engines.

The Internet has information about all of the planets in our solar system. To learn about the nine planets, visit these Web sites:

Encarta Homepage
www.encarta.com
Type the name of a planet that you would like to learn about into the search engine.

NASA Kids
http://kids.msfc.nasa.gov
NASA built a Web site for young learners just like you. Visit this site to learn more about the nine planets, space travel, and the latest NASA news.

Young Scientists at Work

Postcard from Neptune

Voyager 2 flew by Neptune on August 25, 1989. Much of what we know about Neptune comes from this single trip. The following activity will make your imagination soar to the planet Neptune.

You will need:

• thick construction paper

• pencil crayons

Suppose you were aboard *Voyager 2* as it flew by Neptune. What do you think you would see? What would you discover? Write and illustrate a postcard to your friends on Earth. Tell them about your trip to Neptune aboard *Voyager 2.*

What Have You Learned?

How much do you know about Neptune?
Test your knowledge!

1 How many moons does Neptune have?

2 What is the color of Neptune?

3 True or False. Neptune has rings.

4 How many space missions have been to Neptune?

5 Is Neptune a rocky planet or a gas planet?

6 What is the name of the large hole in Neptune's atmosphere?

7 Is it hot or cold on Neptune?

8 What is the name of Neptune's largest moon?

9 Can you see Neptune without a telescope or binoculars?

10 Who is Neptune named for?

What was your score?

9–10	You should work at NASA!
5–8	Not too bad for an earthling!
0–4	You need to polish your telescope!

Answers

1 Neptune has eight moons. **2** Neptune is blue. **3** True. Neptune has four rings. **4** There has been only one mission to Neptune. It was *Voyager 2*. **5** Neptune is a gas planet. **6** The large hole is called the Great Dark Spot. **7** It is cold on Neptune. **8** Neptune's largest moon is Triton. **9** No. You cannot see Neptune without a telescope or binoculars. **10** Neptune is named for the Roman god of the sea.

Words to Know

astronomer: a person who studies space and its objects

atmosphere: the layer of gases that surrounds a planet

climate: the average weather conditions of a place or region

diameter: a straight line passing through the center of a circle, from one side to the other

gravity: a force that pulls things toward the center

mass: a measure of the amount of matter a body contains

mathematician: a person who studies math and numbers

mythology: stories or legends, often about gods or heroes

orbits: the nearly circular paths space objects make around other objects in space

predicted: an educated guess

solar system: the Sun, planets, and other objects that move around the Sun

space probe: a spacecraft used to gather information about space

Index